Catching
the Spider

Catching the Spider

POEMS FOR CHILDREN

John Mole

Illustrated by Anthony Lewis

Blackie Children's Books

BLACKIE CHILDREN'S BOOKS

Published by the Penguin Group
Penguin Books Ltd, 27 Wrights Lane, London W8 5TZ, England
Penguin Books USA Inc., 375 Hudson Street, New York, NY 10014, USA
Penguin Books Australia Ltd, Ringwood, Victoria, Australia
Penguin Books Canada Ltd, 10 Alcorn Avenue, Toronto, Ontario, Canada M4V 3B2
Penguin Books (NZ) Ltd, 182-190 Wairau Road, Auckland 10, New Zealand

Penguin Books Ltd, Registered Offices: Harmondsworth, Middlesex, England

First published 1990 by Blackie Children's Books
This edition first published 1992
10 9 8 7 6 5 4 3 2 1
1 3 5 7 9 10 8 6 4 2

Text copyright © 1990 John Mole
Illustrations copyright © 1990 Anthony Lewis

Made and printed in Great Britain by Butler and Tanner Ltd, Frome and London

A CIP catalogue record for this book is available from the British Library

ISBN   0 216 92864 8
ISBN   0 216 93011 1 Pbk

for
Miriam & Jed Skelton

Acknowledgements

'Nine Riddles' first appeared in *Once There Were Dragons* (Deutsch, 1979) and 'City Station' in *Feeding the Lake* (Secker & Warburg, 1981)

About the Author

John Mole is a distinguished adult and children's poet. His recent collection *Boo to a Goose* (Peterloo Poets, 1987) won the 1988 Signal Award presented annually to an outstanding book of poetry published for children.

Born in Somerset, John Mole now lives with his wife and two sons in Hertfordshire where he writes, teaches, helps to run a printing press and plays regularly as a jazz clarinettist.

Contents

Gran Comes To Stay

May I use the bathroom?
Is anyone in there?
Would you fill my bottle?
I *must* arrange my hair.

My feet are feeling better.
My memory is not.
Where did I put my glasses?
Is the water hot?

I wish they had *two* bathrooms.
They ought to have more space.
The way they don't sit down to meals
Is an absolute disgrace.

I really cannot hurry.
Is it time for tea?
Please don't do a single thing
Especially for me.

This house is full of people.
Children come and go.
I love to have them round me
But oh oh oh

Is that the telephone again?
There's someone at the door.
Don't they ever go to bed?
It's bad for them, I'm sure!

It wasn't like this in my day
But my day isn't theirs.
There'll come a time, though, mark my words . . .
I've left my stick upstairs.

Youth and Age

Someone has gone and left the swing
Still swinging, slowly,
Slower, slow, and now
It stops, and someone else
Is coming.

Someone has gone and left the chair
Still rocking, slowly,
Slower, slow, and now
It stops, and there is silence
In the room.

The Shoes

These are the shoes
Dad walked about in
When we did jobs
In the garden,
When his shed
Was full of shavings,
When he tried
To put the fence up,
When my old bike
Needed mending,
When the car
Could not get started,
When he got up late
On Sunday.
These are the shoes
Dad walked about in
And I've kept them
In my room.

These are not the shoes
That Dad walked out in
When we didn't know
Where he was going,
When I tried to lift
His suitcase,
When he said goodbye
And kissed me,

When he left his door-key
On the table,
When he promised Mum
He'd send a postcard,
When I couldn't hear
His special footsteps.
These are not the shoes
That Dad walked out in
But he'll need them
When he comes back home.

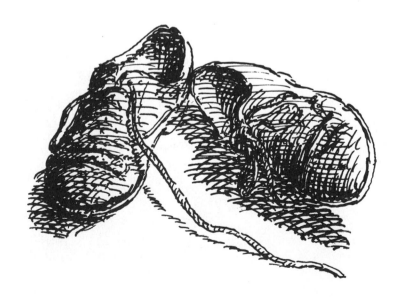

The Wrong Half

Too clever by half
Is less than half of clever
And the wrong half
Like happy without forever
After or laughter
Without the echo
Of laughter
Or love without you.

The Cat on the Wall

The cat on the wall
Lies flat on the wall
And her tail lies even flatter.
She has nothing to do
Except look at you
As if nothing you did could matter.

Just once but no more
She may stretch a limp paw
Then slip out her tongue to clean it.
The cat on the wall
Makes you feel rather small
Though she probably doesn't mean it.

Tiger Rolls

A bakery
In Cornwall sells
Straight-from-the-oven
Tiger Rolls.

Feathery mix
And crispy crust –
Breaking bits off
Is a must,

So lay the jam on
Thick and fast,
Tiger Rolls
Aren't baked to last.

I've heard by someone
It's been said
A poem's like
A loaf of bread,

A necessary
Wholesome food,
Always fresh
And tasting good,

And if that's so
My poem's goal
's to be your favourite
Tiger Roll.

The Morning Bus

is all of us together every schoolday
piling on with Gary shouting 'What's the rush?',

is Craig and Jamie racing for the back
and flattening their mugs against the window,

is Susannah showing off her latest project
with its ticks and stars and exclamation marks,

is Michael like an empty lunch-box
in the front seat sitting on his own,

is Megan reading bits from Judy Blume
to Jo who laughs a lot but isn't listening,

is Tony polishing a cloudy marble
held up to the light with one eye closed,

is Craig and Jamie Enterprises' latest plan
for helping us to spend our pocket-money,

is Samantha always wearing headphones
unattached to anything except her ears,

is all the reasons we can think of
why Amanda's sitting next to Paul,

is reaching school, and Gary's 'What's the rush?',
and Michael waiting till we've all got off.

So What if My Bedroom

IS the biggest mess
You ever saw?
'There ought to be a law
Against it,' Mum says. Yes

Ok, there ought to be a law
But we both know I'd break it
So why can't she just take it
As it comes? What's more

She doesn't *have* to clean it.
I can live with dust
And juice-stains and the crust
Of last week's sandwiches. I mean it,

What's the point of tidiness,
So dull, so always the same,
When a really thorough mess
Can be *you*, like your own name?

Rhymes

Once there was a rat
Who thought he was a mouse
And all he ever did
Was rhyme with House.

Once there was a fork
Which thought it was a spoon
And all it ever did
Was rhyme with June.

Once there was a poet
Whose name was Mole
Which gave him loads of trouble
When he went to school.

How Many Beans?

When I was a kid
I loved this special silly thing
My grandpa said –
He'd sit there scratching
His old bald head
And asking
'How many beans make five?'
As if he hadn't a clue
But guessed that *someone* knew.

Grandpa, if you were alive
Today
I'd say
'Four – plus the one that got away.'

Nine Riddles

1

You should be glad that through the dark
I kept awake; instead
With something like a grunt or bark
You bash me on the head;

Which only goes to show, I'd say,
As sure as I'm wound tight,
That people often break by day
The vows they made last night.

2

The break of day
Shakes out its music
On the battlefield.

We muster our thin forces
As the dangerous
Shadows fall.

Touchdown. Wings
Announce the enemy,
Their fleetest air-arm.

Shrilling bayonets
Invade our trenches, and
The tug of war begins in earnest.

3

Whenever your meat's tough we tear it,
Whenever you're silent we're dumb,
And if we're a long pointed pair it
Could be that Dracula's come.

Whenever you grin we must bear it,
Whenever you're downcast we're glum,
And if you've a brace we must wear it;
We're a mouthful to live with, by gum!

4

Built between man and man
By man, I bear his slogans:
Out! Vote Now! Go Home!
Poor dreamer,
Banging his head against me.

5

Post-haste or slow,
Let there be no doubt
That wherever you go
I shall find you out
At whatever address,
And I mean business.

I'm dull, brown,
And I come at a price;
I watch you frown
With fear or surprise
At a name you know
Through my little window.

To send me again
Don't tear, use a knife
And a different name –
Ah well, it's a life!
Back and forth, back and forth
All over the earth.

6

We sparkle when you smile,
We wobble when you cough,
Sometimes a metre seems a mile
When you take us off.

In rain or sunny weather
When you're tired we're there
To hold your world together,
A very helpful pair.

If you do not need us
We're cushioned in a case
Until your fate has freed us
To perch upon your face.

7

Wrapped in a cloak,
I flash my silver lining;

Cheer up, now,
It's not as bad as that.

I may be dense,
I may be woolly-minded,

But you'll think more clearly
When I'm swept away.

8

I am an elephant, I am a castle.
Come on inside and wet your whistle.

I am a coach complete with horses,
Offering snacks or several courses.

I am a lion, red and white,
Who should be asleep by eleven at night.

I'm a jolly sailor, a poor king's head.
If you haven't guessed yet, have a drink instead.

9

Bag of bones,
Old bony,
Who'd be you for love or money?
Yet for neither love
Nor money,
You'll be mine,
My Bony.

Discs and Dishes

Hearing what I want to hear
I'm happy that the tuning's right
But when reception isn't clear
I blame it on a satellite.

The sky is full of discs and dishes
Thanks to Scientific Man –
Though outer space controls my wishes
Inner space is where I am.

In the Beginning

In the beginning was the echo
Of the end of what had gone before.

In the beginning was the answer
To the question nobody had ever asked.

In the beginning was the satisfaction
Of the hunger of the echo.

In the beginning was the question
Swallowing its easy answer.

In the beginning was the nobody
Who had not been there at the end.

In the beginning only the beginning mattered.
Once it had started everything was easy.

A Stitch in Time

A stitch in time
Sewed up our clock
And made it tick
When it should tock

And when it rained
It didn't pour
Because we'd heard
That one before.

The early bird
Would never wait
To catch the worm
Which came too late

And all the cooks
Were far too few
To spoil the broth
I'd made for you.

The rolling stone
Scraped clean of moss
Never recovered
From its loss

And if you're puzzled
By this rhyme
Blame it on
That stitch in time.

The Bad Dream

'Come in!' calls the dark cave
With a drip drip drip in it.
Watch where you're stepping, be brave,
Be careful,
Don't stumble,
Don't slide or slip in it.

But everything's outside in
And getting deeper.
Oh for just a little pin
To drop
Drop
And wake this sleeper.

Listen, each wall is a huge echo
Bouncing your shout off it,
Promising never, no
Never
Never
You'll never get out of it

Then . . .

'Come home!' calls your clock,
And that pin-point ahead
Through a gap in the rock
Grows larger,
Brighter,
And you're back in bed.

The Christmas Bees

Bees prepare for Christmas,
Bees with glittering wings,
Bees beneath the mistletoe
Kiss each other's stings.

Bees join your party,
Bees rock and jive,
Bees sing buzzy carols
Then collect for their hive.

Bees shine in the moonlight,
Bees fly through the snow,
Bees find your stocking
And hide in its toe.

Bees wake up early,
Bees can never wait,
Bees bother Mum and Dad
Who went to bed late.

Bees open presents,
Bees wear paper hats,
Bees have always wanted this
And this and this and that.

Bees nibble turkey,
Bees watch the Queen on telly,
Bees land on Grandpa's plate
And wobble on his jelly.

Bees clear Christmas lunch away,
Bees wash the dishes,
Bees save the wishbone
But who can guess their wishes?

Bees like icing sugar,
Bees love almond paste,
Bees say 'Hi!' to currants
Because they've got good taste.

Bees are getting tired now,
Bees play silly games,
Bees have had a brilliant day,
It's time for brilliant dreams.

Bees cannot say Thank You,
Bees tickle you instead,
Bees enjoy their Christmas
Then buzz off to bed.

Pet Questions

Does your dog wag its tail
Or its tail wag your dog?
Is your frisky new kitten
A Puss or a Mog?
Is your hamster a gerbil,
Your pig worth a guinea,
Your goggling goldfish
A fatty or thinny?
Why does your parrot shout
'Pieces of Eight!'?
Where does your tortoise go
At such a rate?
And if you should reckon
These questions are mad,
Does your dad nag your mum
Or your mum nag your dad?

Working in Winter

Silently the snow settles on the scaffolding,
The feathery flakes flurry and flick their fragments,
The brown bricks piled on billowing polythene
Heap their heaviness to heavenly heights.
Workmen in woolly hats whistle into the wind
Or dance in donkey jackets to hold in heat,
Their toes tingle, the tips of their fingers freeze –
It's murder, mate, this job is, murder.
Roll on five o'clock!

Instructions for Catching the Spider

1

Slip it between an upturned cup
Or tumbler and a postcard
Carefully slid in under it, remembering
That just because it doesn't buzz
You can't assume
It likes the darkness.

2

Walk to the door
Or nearest window if it opens easily,
Slide back the postcard, let
The light in, gently tip the cup
Or tumbler, wait
Until the spider's ready.

3

Watch it hang a moment
In a web of air
As if somehow attached to it
Before it drifts down, landing
Right-way-up because its legs are everywhere,
And scampers off across the garden.

Foot-Work

Walking down an empty street
Your footsteps argue with your feet.

When your feet speed up you find
Your footsteps want to stay behind

And when your footsteps start to hurry
Your feet become refractory.

Why should a simple evening walk
Set up such overlapping talk?

With all that quickening and slowing
How can you be sure where you're going?

An Invitation

Nobody goes there anymore –
Nobody knows why
It's Open House to nobody
And nobody drops by.

Somebody must have gone there once –
Somebody should know
Something about somebody
Who saw somebody go.

Will anybody come with me –
Will anybody dare
To knock and shout 'Is anybody
ANYBODY there?'

Dolly

I've always called her that
Although there's now not much of her
To put a name to. Well,
Not much resembling anything
You'd recognise unless you loved her.

She's a cloth face without features
Flopping on her chest, a twisted
Knot of arms and legs which dangle
And a sort of body somewhere in the middle
Though there was a time when everyone
Admired her, when she was beautiful enough
For everyone to say, 'She's lovely,
What's her name? If she were mine
I'd call her Cinderella.'

So I think perhaps what love does
Is to dress the friend you dream of
In the finest clothes although she's lost them
And there's only you to see her
When the golden coach arrives, a voice cries
'She's the one!', her floppy foot
Receives the shining slipper
As her arms reach out to thank you
And she dances with the Prince.

The Song-Birds

When William Wordsworth heard the news
Just one thing caused him sorrow.
He didn't have a smart dress-suit
So a suit he had to borrow.

His fame had led Her Majesty
To make him Poet Laureate
'But I haven't got a smart dress-suit,
He cried, 'Who has one? May I borrow it?'

'Of course.' said Samuel Rogers who
Was a full six inches smaller
(Samuel was a poet too
But William was taller).

So he squeezed into that suit
And paid the Queen his visit
And she was too polite to say
'That isn't *your* suit, is it!'

A song-bird in a borrowed suit –
Could any sight be sorrier?
But Wordsworth was a famous man
And she was Queen Victoria.

When Wordsworth died, Lord Tennyson
Took over as PL
And at his own investiture
Wore Samuel's suit as well.

He wore it as a tribute to
That late great Man of Letters
But as he wasn't quite so tall
It fitted him much better.

So when her proud new Laureate
Walked through the Royal door,
The Queen was too polite to say
'I've seen that suit before!'

When Tennyson died, the next PL
Was a man called Alfred Austin.
He wore his own suit on the day
Though we don't know what it cost him.

We don't know, either, much about
His verse. It's been forgotten.
No doubt the Queen thought it was good
But some say it was rotten.

Four Things to Remember
When Writing a Poem

A watched pot
Never boils.

A watched phone
Never rings.

A watched clock
Never strikes.

A watched song
Never sings.

The Waiting Game

Nuts and marbles in the toe,
An orange in the heel,
A Christmas stocking in the dark
Is wonderful to feel.

Shadowy, bulging length of leg
That crackles when you clutch,
A Christmas stocking in the dark
Is marvellous to touch.

You lie back on your pillow
But that shape's still hanging there.
A Christmas stocking in the dark
Is very hard to bear,

So try to get to sleep again
And chase the hours away.
A Christmas stocking in the dark
Must wait for Christmas Day.

A Quick Note from Father Christmas

Great pie,
Thanks mate,
Got to go,
Can't wait,
So many houses
Still to visit,
Not much fun this
Really, is it?
Wife's tired too,
Wants me home,
No joke Santa-ing
On your own.

The Fridge

Into the kitchen
At half-past three
And straight to the fridge –
What's in it for me?

A strawberry yoghurt?
A sticky Swiss Bun?
Oh an Angel Delight
Is my generous Mum!

So I open the door
But a breath of cold air
Is all that I find –
There's nothing there.

Now this really is not
How things should be
When you get home from school
At half-past three.

Water Music

When I whistle in the bath
There's nobody who doesn't know
I'm doing so.

My favourite tune's
An old jazz classic, hotter
Than the water.

What's it called?
Well, I suppose
It's got a name perhaps

Though when you're lying there with both big toes
Stuck half-way up the taps
Names hardly matter.

Lost and Found

In my parents' eyes I see
The child that I was meant to be
But who's gone missing? Them or me?

And who is it owns this tangled ground
Where each of us plays lost and found
Until there's nobody around?

The Lost Ball

Flying up against the sun
The ball goes, and you try
To follow it until the dazzle
Blacks it out, and in the darkness
Someone calls 'Your turn
To fetch it,' and you run
Through gradual light
To where you think it went
But when you turn again to check
The angle that it came from
All you find is emptiness
And silence where your friends were
Who have upped and gone
Or were they ever there, you wonder,
As the sun goes in
And who is this you
Thought was you who
Scrabbles among earth, long grass
And brambles, looking for a ball
Which maybe no one ever threw
And never landed?

The City Station

Here is an avenue of welcome,
Open arms and long embrace –
'How was the journey? My, you have grown!'
While each minute hides its face.

Here is an endless strip of sadness,
Find your handkerchief and cry –
'Don't forget us. Write soon. God bless – '
While the huge clock wipes its eye.

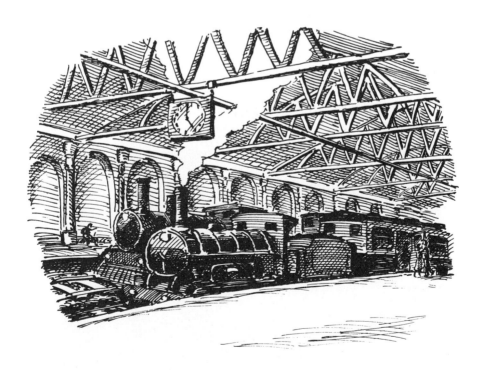

The Whisper

Around the world the whisper goes,
A gentle, universal breath,
And everything that hears it grows.

At its command the river flows,
A blade of light, a glittering sheath –
Around the world the whisper goes.

What it is saying no one knows
Although it tells of life not death
And everything that hears it grows.

It takes the measure of its foes,
It makes a garland of a wreath –
Around the world the whisper goes.

It fills with hope the wind that blows
Across the desolated heath
And everything that hears it grows.

Above us all it still bestows
A blessing on what lies beneath.
Around the world the whisper goes
And everything that hears it grows.

Spring Clean

Clean up!
Roared the universe
This room
Is a disgrace!

And sweetly muttering
Of course
A shamed flower
Hid its face.

Answers to Riddles

1. Alarm Clock
2. Worms
3. Teeth
4. Wall
5. Envelope
6. Spectacles
7. Cloud
8. Pub
9. Skeleton

Index of First Lines